Miscarriage and Early Baby Loss

 caring for yourself and others

Dedication
For Sinead and for all our babies in heaven

Miscarriage and Early Baby Loss

caring for yourself and others

Breda Theakston

redemptorist
publications

Published by Redemptorist Publications
Alphonsus House, Chawton, Hampshire, GU34 3HQ, UK
Tel: +44 (0)1420 88222, Fax: +44 (0)1420 88805
Email: rp@rpbooks.co.uk, www.rpbooks.co.uk

A registered charity limited by guarantee
Registered in England 3261721

Copyright © Redemptorist Publications 2018
First published March 2018

Series Editor: Sister Janet Fearns
Edited by Kathy Dyke
Designed by Eliana Thompson

ISBN 978-0-85231-516-3

The publisher gratefully acknowledges permission to use the following copyright material: Excerpts from the *New Revised Standard Version Bible*: Anglicised Edition, © 1989, 1995, Division of Christian Education of the National Council of the Churches of Christ in the United States of America. Used by permission. All rights reserved.

Every effort has been made to trace copyright holders and to obtain their permission for the use of copyright material. The publisher apologises for any errors or omissions and would be grateful for notification of any corrections that should be incorporated in future reprints or editions of this book.

Printed by Lithgo Press Ltd.,
Leicester, LE8 6NU

Foreword

I am extremely grateful to everyone who gave of their time to talk to me about their experience of miscarriage and early baby loss. I promised anonymity but you know who you are – thank you for your honest and generous sharing.

Thank you to Dr Bella Noel, obstetrician and gynaecologist, and to Jane Hay, midwife, who helped in their professional capacities. I am particularly grateful to Gail Sainsbury and to Sr Janet Fearns for believing I could do this and to Linda Pennington and other colleagues and friends who gave me moral support in one way or another.

My greatest debt is to our sons, Thomas, Edmund and Henry, who have grown into fine young men despite my tendency towards neurotic parenting, and most especially to Kevin, who lived all this with me and who looked after me with encouragement and patience while I hid away to try to write the unwritable.

This is a very personal perspective but it was also written in the hope that it would give some comfort to those who experience any early baby loss. It is necessarily partial and incomplete. For each one of us, our experience of loss is unique.

I could not have written this without lots of help but all errors are entirely my own.

1

Miscarriage: what is it?

The basic medical definition of miscarriage as "the loss of a pregnancy during the first twenty-three weeks" is clear and simple but probably utterly belies the depth and breadth of the experience the woman, her spouse or partner and family actually go through.[1] The stark reality for you, if you have had a miscarriage, a stillbirth or a neonatal death, is that you were pregnant and you expected a child, and now you are not pregnant but you do not have your child to hold. This is a bereavement.

Definitions are important and the best people to advise you on the practicalities of your own experience are your medical carers. They can guide you in important after-the-event details like registering the birth/death and funeral options, including using the hospital's "forget-me-not" memorial garden. They will also be able to point the way to future care and pregnancies and to local bereavement services.

But when I speak of miscarriage and baby loss here, I mean to include all baby loss, however incurred, but without going into the details of the medical facts or context. I do this to try to help all who undergo such an early loss to tease out what it actually means to us and how and why it is important that we experience what has happened and find a way to live with it. Not all baby loss is acknowledged and my aim here is to try to show how damaging it can be to fail to recognise its impact, not only on the woman but on all her relationships and any future children she may have. As I write, I have in my mind and in my heart my own experiences of baby loss, including four miscarriages and one neonatal death, a long time ago.

Inevitably I write from my own experience and perspective. Yours will be different but I hope something here helps you and those around you to know the truth of what you are experiencing and to help you through it.

Feelings

The first and most important thing a woman needs following a miscarriage is to ensure that she is well and physically recovering.

Of at least equal, if not greater, importance is your emotional and mental well-being. Sometimes, especially in the context of a medical event or procedure, you may worry that your feelings may seem out of place, and it may be very difficult for you to allow yourself to express what you really feel.

You may have heard the miscarriage spoken of as a "fetus", a "failed pregnancy" or as the natural loss of a "chromosomally abnormal" pregnancy. However accurate it may be medically, this language can blind us to the true extent of our loss. It can make it difficult to know why you feel as you do or to acknowledge your feelings. The truth is that while a miscarriage can appear, from the outside, to be a relatively minor medical event, it may be seismic for you.

Baby loss, even at the very earliest stage, is a bereavement and, like all bereavements, it is likely to affect us in strong, strange and maybe shocking ways. It is very important, as soon after the miscarriage as possible, that you find a way to allow your feelings, however awful. Whatever you are feeling is true for you, and needs, if possible, to find expression – this is the work of grieving.

Grieving, or mourning, is very difficult work indeed. But your feelings about what happened are real and allowing them to be, if you can bear it, will help your healing. It takes as long as it takes. There is no easy way, and there is no road map. Family and friends may help but they may not be the best listeners. They may feel overwhelmed themselves and you may need to contact someone else, someone with experience of baby loss themselves or a trained grief counsellor. Even years later, if you have experienced a baby loss that you were unable to grieve, you may need to find someone to talk to who will help you to experience and mourn your loss.

Loss

A miscarriage is a loss. You had a baby and now you do not. Grief is pain that our bodies register when we suffer loss. It is a very important human emotion and process, but one that no one ever wants to face. You may not even understand why you feel so wretched, and you may want to find ways to avoid or to run away from the pain. We all do that to some extent. Yet, while grieving is a deeply uncomfortable process, both to experience and to witness in others, being fully aware of and fully experiencing their feelings will, paradoxically, help the person who has suffered the loss.

Grieving is not for the faint-hearted. Although, if you are faint-hearted, take heart. I was too. I did not really grieve well, partly because it was difficult to find people who could cope with the awfulness of my pain. Miscarriage is a hidden loss and at the time I did not fully understand the enormity of what had happened. It did not help that I had been brought up to hide pain. But I did what I could and that is all any of us can do. The immediate sorrow and pain subsided over the years but the wounds remain hidden, just under the skin as it were and liable to be ripped open again in a moment if there is other trauma or loss.

However hard it is, the work of grief is better done than not done. So (and I know that this may be too difficult for you now) try to resist the temptation to shut your feelings down or to put them off until a more convenient time. There is no good time to grieve. Grief interrupts our life and demands our attention. Give it the attention it needs. Grief that is not acknowledged will not go away, even if we try to ignore the signals from our bodies, hearts and minds. When we do not grieve we carry that unresolved pain with us for ever. It is never too late though, as we will see.

If you have experienced baby loss your challenge is immense and you will need all the help you can get. If you care for someone who has experienced a miscarriage, know that it is not just a minor medical event: it potentially carries much more significance, and therefore much more pain, than you can imagine.

What does miscarriage mean to you?

Your feelings are your best clue to what your miscarriage, or baby loss, means to you. You honour yourself and your child when you allow yourself to feel the full force of agony that accompanies the loss. It will not go on for ever, although it might feel like that now. If you can, talk to someone, or find some other way to articulate the unspeakable pain you feel. It will help you to come to an understanding of what the baby meant to you and to remember what happened, and what it meant to you, in ways that suit you and that will help you in the future.

Not all women experience miscarriage as a trauma. How you feel about the miscarriage will be the clue to what it means for you, and your feelings might surprise you. If you were happy to be expecting a child then the loss may feel huge. If you were not happy, or if you were ambivalent about the pregnancy, your feelings may be more complex – a mixture of regret, sadness and relief. Whatever your feelings, miscarriage is a significant event for any woman and your feelings need to be acknowledged, allowed and respected.

The importance of grief

I had no idea what grief was when I lost my babies through miscarriage so I tried to live as if nothing had happened. I now know that it is good to pay attention to what you feel, to accept what you feel, and to accept that you may feel very different things at very different times. This will be easier for some people than others, but try to name your feelings if you can and allow them fair expression.

If you find it difficult to access, to name or to express your feelings, you may need to find a sensitive and skilled grief counsellor to help you. It is important that the work of grief is done and is done at the pace that is right for you. There is no standard pattern. It is what it is. Everyone is different. Trust yourself and your own feelings, not what someone else, even in a guide like this, tells you to feel.

There are books on grief and its stages but, in real life, we do not "feel" according to textbook stages. So, if you find something on grief that suggests you will go through so many stages, in such and such an order and that it will take so long, beware – this description is culled and simplified from a huge number of experiences of grief. Your grieving process will not look like that.

How you do the "feelings work" or "grieving" will depend on your unique personality. It will depend on your life experiences and on your family of origin and how they handled feelings, especially hard and painful feelings. It will depend on your context, who shares your life, who knows about what has happened, and on their ability to handle feelings of sadness. If you were brought up in an emotionally literate family which has healthy communication habits, respectful of feelings, then you will be in a better position to express your feelings, however ugly they are, and to construct a narrative that will serve you as "the story of my baby" for the rest of your life.

You might find that your sadness over losing your baby is complicated by the unexpected surfacing of grief and perhaps anger associated with completely unrelated events which took place in your past. If your baby loss brings to the fore earlier, possibly unacknowledged, losses or traumas it is worth exploring these too. This may be where finding professional help will be both very helpful and very necessary.

This is what the work of grief involves: feeling it, naming it, and telling the story of, or remembering, your pregnancy, your baby. All these are essential for healing. As you allow your feelings it can help to record the feelings and what emerges for you. This can be done in any way that feels right for you: in words, paint, music, dance, needlework, knitting, pottery... whatever medium you prefer.

The mother who feels the miscarriage as the loss of a whole person needs to allow the feelings that flow from such a loss.

"We had the experience but missed the meaning..."

T.S. Eliot, "The Dry Salvages",
Four Quartets

If we do not allow our feelings at the moment and in the days, weeks and months ahead, we may deny ourselves the chance to remember and tell the story if we wish. Being able to tell the story of what happens to us is a key to our own development as human beings. Remembering is crucial to integrating that experience of pregnancy, the expected child and the loss of that child into our larger life story.

Why is it important that we can do this? Allowing ourselves to experience our grief is not, as I was taught, just a self-indulgent emoting. It is a vital part of our spiritual growth. In his book on depression and spirituality, author Tim Farrington says:

> We are often encouraged to buck up, to get over it, and so to throw out the baby of the slow true process of grieving with the bathwater. Grief will never go away, if we're really paying attention. It's part of being awake: we love, and we lose those we love to the erosions of time, sickness, and death (until those we love lose us to the same). To lose a loved one is to be called to come to genuine terms with that loss, or risk losing touch with that in us which loved.[2]

It is important because it helps us, over time, to heal in our own hearts and minds. (By "heal" I do not mean "forget", I mean learn to live with.) And grieving really can take a long time. How we manage our grief is also very important because it can have an impact on any future children. Our sons were born soon after our daughter died, and I had not properly grieved for her. I was afraid of piling a whole heap of pain on them and tried very hard not to be affected, but it is not possible to control our emotions. They still noticed, even though they probably did not know what was wrong.

The problem is that grieving can take a very long time. However, the truth is that avoiding grief is not an answer. Trying to avoid the grieving process is like trying to turn our hearts off. If we succeed we do so at too great a cost. As W.B. Yeats said in his poem "Easter, 1916":

> "Too long a sacrifice
> can make a stone of the heart."

Do not be surprised if the pain of grief rises and bites you unexpectedly even long after the event. What we learn may also enable us to help, and perhaps accompany, other women in their experience of early baby loss. At the very least, our experience can help us, in the manner described by W.B. Yeats in *The Cloths of Heaven*, to "tread softly".

Endnotes

1. www.nhs.uk/conditions/miscarriage/Pages/Introduction.aspx

2. Tim Farrington, *A Hell of Mercy: a meditation on depression and the dark night of the soul* (New York: Harper One, 2009), 47.

2

For those who suffer

The mother

Because we cannot see the baby whose life is lost, the centre of attention is always the woman whose body experiences the miscarriage. After physical healing, the really difficult part of the loss begins. I wish there were a way to take this away from you, but there isn't. You have suffered the loss and now you also need to find the strength within you to assert your right to feel what you feel and to give meaning to your experience – a tall order, yes, but essential.

The people around us are critical to helping us to do this. If they can bear our grief, if they are able to accept us when we cry, to affirm us, to help us to actually experience those feelings without hurrying, or belittling, or trying to "reframe" it to cheer us up, they become compassionate companions in our healing.

It might help, as soon as you can after the loss, to create something beautiful for your baby. You do not need special skills. Do what feels right for you and make it special for your baby. This will help in the future when you come to remember and share the story.

Ultimately each woman who miscarries, for whatever reason, has to confront what the pregnancy meant to her. What hopes and dreams had she invested in her baby? How will she remember the pregnancy and loss? How will she talk of it? Miscarriage may be more than the loss of a baby: it may be the loss of her dream of a family.

She may have longed for a baby for some time. She may have been through lots of waiting and disappointment before this pregnancy. She may have had several other miscarriages or baby losses. She may have felt that this pregnancy was her last hope of a family. Or she may have felt horrified to discover the pregnancy and now feels some relief that it is over – not all women weave positive dreams and expectations around a pregnancy. From the outside others simply cannot tell if any of this is true for you.

"There's no art to find the mind's construction in the face..."

Shakespeare,
Macbeth I.iv

We are all different. You may not feel sad all the time. You may slide back easily and gratefully into a happy and busy life after the miscarriage. Or you may struggle to stay afloat amidst your clamouring feelings.

The energy with which painful or frightening feelings suddenly hit you, apparently out of the blue, in the days, weeks and months after a miscarriage may surprise you. These feelings are painful but, paradoxically, precious – they are your guide to meaning and to recovery. So, if you can, acknowledge them and stay with them for long enough to think about how you might describe them.

This is what people mean when they say people are "in mourning". These awful feelings that appear to assail you are not an interruption to life. They are your life at this moment. They are your legitimate, human and essential way of experiencing loss. Grieving is a process that takes its own time. It is never easy. You have the right and freedom to do it in your own time, and in your own way.

Not everyone wants to talk but some find it really helpful. Find someone who is willing to be a compassionate friend, who can listen, really listen, without telling you what you should or should not be doing; someone who can be with you in a kind, supportive and accepting way as you bear your own devastating pain.

As you learn from your feelings, reading, conversations, research, viewing, meditation or any other exploration what your miscarriage means to you, you can discover its own narrative. Once you have a story you will then be in a position to share it with other people.

This feeling, telling and discovering of the narrative will probably all happen in a jumble and over time. That's okay. Life is not clockwork – it is messy and unexpected and very little gets done when we want it to, or as well as it could be. If what I write sounds too neat it is only because I have to impose some order. If it sounds incoherent, that is what grief feels like.

Our resistance to experiencing the pain and our refusal to discover the story or to want to express it or share it with anyone are all human responses. It is natural to want to avoid the pain of grief. No one wants it. Jesus was in agony at the thought of what he would go through.

Opening up

After your loss you will have to decide whom to tell. Not everyone needs to know. It is a judgement call only you can make. Telling becomes easier if you are helped to do the hard work of grief in the very earliest days. Expressing your experience and feelings in any medium will help you when you want to tell someone. A priest or pastor may be able to help you and your spouse or partner to articulate what you are feeling. You may well cry buckets the first time you speak of it, or write it. But with someone caring, who can listen with compassion and without judgement, you will be able to share your story appropriately.

Deciding whom to tell is not a just a one-off decision but one you will encounter, usually in unexpected ways, throughout the rest of your life. For me one of the most difficult questions to answer, even all these years later, is "How many children do you have?" In my mind and in my heart, and in reality, I have eight children (four lost in miscarriages, one daughter who died at eight days and three live and lovely grown-up sons). The other difficult one is when people see our sons and say, jovially enough, "What, no daughters!" Each time I have to make a split-second decision about how much to share.

It is okay not to speak of your loss. But it can create wonderful new bonds in unexpected places if you do decide to share. Be prepared, though, for the fact that not everyone has experienced such a loss and not everyone will know how to respond.

How people react may be critical for how you remember what has happened. So find people you trust to listen and to accept your feelings without dismissing them or trying to jolly them away with positive reframing. There will be a time for new perspectives, but right now you need to be accepted where you are.

People may unwittingly say something trite or crass in the hope of making you feel better. When this happens it can be hugely painful. They will almost certainly be people of goodwill who just cannot see the extent of your loss. This is the hard burden of early baby loss: no one who has not had a miscarriage or early baby loss can really understand. Yet their innocent inability to recognise our still tender feelings can be excruciating. The truth is that grief never goes away but we do learn, however awkwardly and imperfectly, to live with it.

Sometimes people will do and say the wrong things. Sometimes people will not be there for you or will neglect or unintentionally hurt you. They may, as Jesus on the cross cried of those who had put him there, simply not know what they are doing.

The basic principle of disclosure is that what happens to you is essentially yours. You choose when and with whom to share it. There are, though, situations when it is better to tell than to keep it to yourself. Tell anyone you need to get access to medical or other help for your body and mind.

Although I can imagine circumstances in which telling nobody may be an option, think twice before deciding upon this.

> "No man is an island,
> entire of itself,
> every man is a piece of the continent,
> a part of the main.
> If a clod be washed away by the sea,
> Europe is the less,
> as well as if a promontory were,
> as well as if a manor of thy friend's
> or of thine own were.

Any man's death diminishes me,
because I am involved in mankind,
and therefore never send to know for whom
the bell tolls;
it tolls for thee."

John Donne,
Meditation XVII

We are relational beings and our experience of life is helped when we share our stories.

However you felt about it, and however it ended, your pregnancy happened and you are entitled to your own feelings about it. It may well have been, as some will say, a "bundle of cells", but it was yours. So, difficult as it may be, do your best to ignore words, however kindly meant, that seek to deny the reality of your loss and your pain.

If you do feel strong enough, when someone, trying to be kind, says something that seeks to move you away from your experience before you are ready, say something like, "Thank you, but that is not helpful to me right now" or, "I need someone to listen." Or even, "I need someone I can cry with."

You might want to phrase your response in a more positive way. You may want to say something like, "I would really like to be able to share this with you but right now I just need to cry. I am sorry if that is difficult for you." Or, "I know it is difficult for you to see me in pain. But the only thing that makes my pain worse is having it ignored."

Your spouse, partner or best friend would be the obvious first person to share this with. Even in the best relationships a partner may well struggle to know what you want and need. So they may need you to talk quite explicitly about what you are feeling, what the loss means to you and about anything that may cause you extra distress. Listen to what they have to say too – they will also have their own feelings of loss.

It is not easy, but try to share rather than hide your pain.[1] Find time to be with each other in a safe space where you have time to talk and cry. As we talk to one another and share our ideas, thoughts and dreams, our knowledge of ourselves and of each other grows. If you cannot talk to each other, try asking for help from a trusted person, a priest, pastor, spiritual guide, professional grief counsellor, Marriage Care, Relate or other relationship counselling organisations.[2]

Should we tell the children?

If you have other children they will need to know that, while something really big has happened and Mummy and Daddy are sad right now, at a fundamental level the world is good and things are going to find a new equilibrium where everything is, while not the same as before, at least all right. How much you tell them depends on their ages and understanding and your relationship with them. It's a tough call. Talk to someone if you are unsure.[3]

It may not be easy but be reassured that you will find your own right words for them. It might be something simple like: "The baby inside me died and is not there any longer" or, "I was pregnant but I am not pregnant any longer." Say something that shares your feelings about your miscarriage: "It sometimes happens and I feel very sad about it" or, "I was looking forward to having a new baby and feel really upset about it."

One important function of the family, which is sometimes known the first "school of humanity", is to help children to survive and thrive. This must include helping us to come to terms with loss. In our family of origin we learn this over time and in all kinds of ways: when we do not get the sweets, chocolate, or toys we ask for; when someone at school hurts us; or when a beloved pet dies.

How these early life experiences are handled as we are growing up, and how we were taught how to handle them for ourselves, will affect how well we are able to experience grief as adults. So, whether, and how, you share this news with your children will be a very important part of their formation.

Remember, feelings are natural. They arise in our bodies before they are registered by our minds. We need to learn from them. Of course you will need to help your child not to "act out" their painful feelings – this is especially important if it is likely to endanger their own or another's lives and limbs. However, it is vital to affirm that, yes, they are feeling bad and it is not easy to bear bad feelings, but you are there for them. We know that life contains both good and bad and they will learn that too.

Schools can help if staff are sensitive to the importance of emotions in a child's learning. Your school may have a Rainbows team or similar organisation working with children suffering any kind of loss.[4] A school may have good reconciliation processes, from listening and saying "sorry" to restorative practice.[5] Schools that understand attachment and attachment teaching can also help a child where family (dis)connectedness is having an impact on their ability to learn or to function well at school.[6]

If your other children have been excitedly expecting a new brother or sister, and feeling the baby move, they too may feel a frightening anguish that they are not able to express. So you will have the double challenge of feeling your own pain and being there for them as they express theirs. Offer them words that might reflect what they feel like: "Does it feel scary?"; "It can feel frightening"; "When someone we love dies it can really hurt in our hearts."

Children need to find appropriate vocabulary for what they are feeling. People sometimes do not want to "feed" children words about difficult feelings in case it stimulates those very feelings. But children need to know that there *is* a word for what they are almost certainly feeling. Unregistered pain is not good for anyone and can be very damaging to children.

Surprisingly, children tend to recognise when a word or phrase is right for them and, be reassured, they will not agree with anything that does not seem to fit. If this is difficult for you talk to someone. Get help. Speak to their other carers at their nursery or school.

Books and films can help. It's okay to cry in front of children but let them cry too. They need to know it is normal for people to feel sad when they lose a baby. Suggest they make their own memento and support them if that is what they would like to do.

Colleagues, neighbours, acquaintances? Tell anyone you wish who you think will be able to hear you with understanding. But tell only if you want to and only if telling will help you. For instance, you might need to let a colleague know if you need time off. You may find that they have experience of a miscarriage or baby loss themselves and so can understand and help you back into the workplace. But remember, it happened to you. It is your right to share or not to share your sadness.

The father

If you are the spouse or partner of a woman who has had a miscarriage you have an onerous role. You are also a bereaved parent. The child that was lost is also your child. Your grief in some ways is more complicated than the mother's grief because you have lost your child and have witnessed, or are witnessing, the aftermath of the loss in the woman you love.

Bearing one another's grief is one of the hardest acts of love we are ever called upon to make. Somehow, the hurt of those we love seems so much harder for us to witness than any hurt we experience ourselves. This is a mystery of being human. It is what makes men's burdens around any fertility or reproductive difficulty particularly testing.

Your task as the father is multi-fold. Firstly, you have to support your wife or partner, physically and emotionally, as she endures and recovers from the miscarriage. Her body is the host and is the one that goes through the process of physical loss. Because it happens in and to her body, your wife, partner or girlfriend necessarily becomes the centre of attention. The need for you to be strong and to support your loved one may make you repress your own grief. This is not unusual but it would be a real loss.

Secondly you have to take time to register your own feelings as this is happening. You may go into emotional shut down and "action man" mode as you deal with the immediate issue of the miscarriage itself. You may feel surprised, shocked even, at the suddenness and the intensity of your pain. In all the necessary concern for your wife/partner you may feel that your feelings are ignored or that your own feelings have no legitimacy, that they mark you out as somehow "odd".

Your feelings are valid and you have a right to them and a right to express them, to share them. Your loss is not the same as your wife's loss. You are two unique individuals with your own unique personalities and ways of handling difficult and painful situations. And, despite your closeness, you and your wife do not stand in exactly the same relation to the miscarriage. The loss affected her directly and may have put her at physical risk.

When someone we love dies, there is usually some community comfort to be had from family and friends who knew them, who have their own memories of them to share with you so you are able to laugh and cry together, each recognising the wholeness, the full living reality of the person who has died. When a baby dies before, or soon after, birth very few people will have had the privilege of meeting them. This means that early baby loss is a particularly lonely loss for parents to bear.

When there is no one else except each other with whom to share the loss, it can have its own difficulties as well as blessings. In a marriage or intimate partnership your feelings will not always be in sync with each other. Our feelings take us by surprise. One moment you may feel fine and think, "I'm over it", and the very next moment (or day, or week or month) feel a sickening constriction of the heart and gut as you once again experience the visceral, the lonely, the devastating pain of a loss that can never be undone.

Even if you are a couple who are highly skilled at loving, intimate, listening communication you may find yourselves inadvertently at odds at moments, especially as the days wear on and the ordinary busy-ness of your daily life and demands intrude more and more insistently.

"...as two spent swimmers, that do cling together and choke their art."

Shakespeare,
Macbeth I.ii

Try not to struggle alone. Get help. Talk to someone or contact a blog for grieving dads.[7]

The truth is that miscarriage is a hidden grief in a lot of people's lives. It is estimated that one in four pregnancies end in miscarriage. That means that at least some of your friends and colleagues will have experienced a miscarriage, or that of their wife or partner. They may also have found it difficult to bear the burden alone and may be glad to listen to your story, as you may also benefit from hearing theirs.

When listening to other people's stories, beware of thinking, "That's not how it was for us," and then worrying that somehow you are not doing it right. Your story is your story. It is not going to be like anyone else's: it cannot be. You are different people, in a different place at a different time. The only commonality is that a pregnancy that was, is no longer. So, listen, but also tell your story. It will be, it must be, different. Telling your story is one way for you to process the grief and to remember.

You have to grieve too

After the drama, maybe the quiet drama, of the miscarriage, you may find yourself wondering why you feel so wretched. However it happened, you have suffered the loss of your baby and that event has become part of your life story. The more difficult part is in the days after. Your wife or partner may or may not be recovering well physically and her health is always a top concern that will need to be established as soon as possible. But then there is the emotional fall-out, which may be sudden, unexpected and leave her, and you, weeping at the most awkward times.

Some people have been taught, however implicitly, that "boys don't cry". This can lead to boys growing into men who find it hard to express, and talk about, their feelings even when, in their hearts, they are torn apart with grief. "Doing something" such as going to a football match, playing a game of golf or working overtime might be the way in which a bereaved father handles his pain. Your wife or partner might find it hard to recognise that you are equally sad, but unable to communicate and tackle your grief as she may be doing.

Try to create the conditions in which you can open your hearts to one another. This is not easy, especially if you have other children. Get help if you think that your different grieving is making a significant dent in your relationship. Marriage Care, Relate and other relationship counselling organisations offer both individual and couple counselling and the earlier you get help the better.[8]

A Zambian proverb, "You never know when a tortoise is dancing", may be helpful: just because the baby's father does not show his pain externally, it does not mean that, internally, he's not just as much of an emotional wreck as his wife. Not knowing how to express his agony and turmoil does not mean that he is not feeling it. Far from it.

In the future you may have a child who in turn experiences miscarriage or baby loss. Allowing your feelings now, naming them and telling yourself what they mean to you will help you if you ever need to be there for them in such a trauma. Because miscarriage is a trauma. For your wife or partner it is a physical trauma and for you both it is the trauma of the loss of your baby, a bereavement.

Endnotes

1. http:/Abstract on "The complexity of couple communication in bereavement" at: http://www.ncbi.nlm.nih.gov/pubmed/24501858

2. http://www.marriagecare.org.uk; www.relate.org.uk

3. https://www.mariecurie.org.uk/help/support/bereaved-family-friends/supporting-grieving-child

4. www.rainbows.org

5. https://restorativejustice.org.uk/restorative-practice-schools

6. https://the-arc.org.uk/

7. https://grievingdads.com/blog/

8. http://www.marriagecare.org.uk; www.relate.org.uk

3

For those who care

The mother is central but the effect of a miscarriage goes beyond her. Just as the baby was attached to the mother for its life, so we are all attached, albeit in less physically direct ways, to each other. We can imagine circles of attachment radiating out from that new life: the mother; her spouse or the father of her child; her other children; parents; siblings; friends; fellow parishioners; colleagues; neighbours. Each person will have their own web of connectedness.

It is this web of connectedness, the many and varied relationships we all have, that helps us to grow through life and keeps us safe and well, in so far as any human being can be kept safe. Our experience of miscarriage and baby loss will affect the people in our web of connectedness in various ways, even though they do not know or cannot see it.

The mother's feelings may be more powerful, irregular and confusing than anyone might have expected. The further away we are from the miscarriage and the woman who has experienced it, the harder it can be for us to see it for what it is to her.

Medical staff

I cannot imagine how difficult it must be to be a medical professional and to have to support a person who is losing or has lost a pregnancy. On the one hand, they are medically trained professionals. On the other, they are people with their own hopes, fears and beliefs about life and love and loss. Their training may have helped them to cope with the human/professional aspects of their work but whatever happens, it is always hard to be with someone who is grieving.

Medical staff and carers need to be aware of their own feelings about what has happened as well as very sensitive to the feelings of the woman in their care and her spouse or partner. As one midwife said,

"I've seen many miscarriages, stillbirths and neonatal deaths but it won't help anyone if I burst into floods of tears on the ward. I've had to learn to become strong without becoming hard. If I ever reach the stage when I can't cry, then I will immediately give up midwifery – but I must not be in such an emotional state in the labour ward that I can't help a couple or carry out my job to the best professional standards needed in the situation."

On the whole, it is best not to presume. Be open to their experience, understanding and prepared to listen. What will almost certainly be true is that the woman you are now caring for will not experience this miscarriage lightly. Even if she did not want to be pregnant, at some level she may have thought of the life within her as a baby and she may feel that in not wanting this baby it was not that she did not want a child but that, at this time and in this place in her life, she could not cope with what a baby means in terms of commitment.

If your professional context does not offer specialised support for these difficult situations, your colleagues will probably be more than happy to help you in a more informal, peer support, way.

Grandparents

Grandparents have a very special, and a particularly difficult, place when a miscarriage happens.[1] This is your grandchild who has died and your beloved child who has suffered this terrible loss. Given the necessary privacy and intimacy of early loss, your grieving child may not come directly to you for comfort. If the couple appears to cling to each other and not want to talk to you, it can feel like you have a double loss: the loss of your grandchild and then the separation from your child as the couple turn to each other in their grief instead of to you.

This may be very difficult to bear and exacerbate any upset you already feel about the loss of your grandchild. The twin demands of dealing with your own grief and dealing with the feelings and reactions of your son or daughter who has just experienced the miscarriage or early baby loss can be very taxing. You may need all the help you can get to cope in the days, weeks and months after such a loss.

Is there a Catholic Grandparents Association or other grandparents' support group near you? If not why not see if you can set one up? [2] These are not specifically for miscarriage, but are places where all grandparents can meet, talk, and perhaps pray for themselves and for their families.

If your daughter or son has a spouse or partner they may not want to talk to anyone else immediately. But there may come a day when they do want to talk and do need some outside support. So try not to take their behaviour to heart. Be patient. Be kind. Be aware that it may not go smoothly and feathers may be ruffled.

Your daughter or son and their spouse or partner will need you in the future. They might need you now if there are children to be looked after. They may worry about sharing too much of their pain with you, not because they want to shut you out, but because they want to protect you from the ugliness of the pain they feel.

One of your tasks as parents and grandparents is to help them to bear their pain. That does not mean for them to bear it alone, to keep it private. Far from it. It means to help and encourage them, if they wish, to talk about their baby, to share, if they can, their dreams and the story of their loss. Don't worry if they don't want to – everyone is different.

You still have huge emotional influence over your children and they may need you to let them know that it is okay to cry. Their feelings will not be pretty and may come in waves. Sometimes the bereaved parents seem fine and then, all of a sudden, they will burst into tears or go silent. If they cry, please let them. You can hold them, sit with them and offer a hanky, but do not try to hurry them to stop crying. Their tears will pierce your heart but they are a very real expression of the love they feel for the child that they have lost, for your grandchild. Be glad that your children have grown into such loving people.

If you can, and this is really difficult, listen. Then listen some more. They may say nothing but just need to weep. Let them weep in your loving, listening, sympathetic presence. I know that this is not easy! It is almost counterintuitive to let our children feel their pain, and especially difficult when you have your own pain.

If you worry that expressing their feelings will just make them worse, be reassured. It won't. Expressing their feelings is exactly what they need to do to come to terms with their loss. If you can't face their grief directly, you may be able to help in practical ways by cooking, shopping, cleaning or fielding calls for them if they ask you to do so, but you cannot control how they feel or how long the grieving process will last before they are ready, gradually, to let go of the visceral raging pain and find ways to remember the pregnancy with love.

As grandparents, however close you are emotionally, physically you are at a slight remove from the loss. It can be a very unexpected and distressing pain to discover that, while everyone is concerned with the mum and the dad, no one notices that your heart is breaking too. If you find it difficult to acknowledge your own feelings you might want to find help. Contact your church or the Miscarriage Association[3] for links to support for grandparents.

When we were young perhaps miscarriage was not recognised as a significant loss. You may not have experienced such a loss. Or you may have experienced a miscarriage earlier in your own life and found people unsympathetic. It may be that now is your time to get help to do your own grieving.[4] Your parish priest may be able to help, and your GP can refer you to local counselling or other services in your area.

The reality is that no one expects a miscarriage and no one in these situations knows exactly the right thing to do or say. How you and your family deal with the miscarriage will depend on the relationship you already have with them. You may live far apart but be very close and trusting with each other. Or you may live very close and yet not be on very intimate terms.

Please be gentle with yourself. If you do not know what to do or to say, then admit it. It really helps to acknowledge that the miscarriage is so big and so real that it is actually bigger than the words at your disposal. You don't need to offer anything more than, "I am so sorry, but I do not know what to say... How are you?" Or, "I wish I knew what to say or do, is there anything you would like right now? What would you like to do that would help you to grieve/ remember her/him?" Helping them to feel and to remember will mean so much to them in the future.

If, in the excitement of the news that they were pregnant, you knitted or bought something for the baby, think about what you want to do with it. Maybe your son or daughter would like it to be part of their memory box. Maybe you will want to keep it for yours.

Help them to remember

Encourage your daughter or son to have a small service or a Mass for the baby at which all these now precious mementoes can be offered before being stored somewhere safe. If your children feel shy of approaching the church, especially if they have not been attending, offer to organise it for them but be sensitive to their wishes – they may feel very strongly that this is not how they want to memorialise their loss.

They need to find their own way to celebrate that short life and remember it. You can remember in your own way and you can always ask for your grandchild to be remembered at a church service you attend. The bereaved parents are probably feeling completely lost, with no idea what to do. If you can suggest anything that the church has to offer and be willing to act as a mediator with your priest or pastor that will be a great help... but only if they want it.

Please do not take offence if your children prefer not to bring their grief to the church. God already knows what they and you are suffering. You can turn to God yourself and ask that all their sighs and tears are held in his embrace, along with yours.

Family, friends and others

If you imagine a radius of impact from a pregnant woman outwards, you will know where to locate yourself on this mental map of connectivity to the person you know who has suffered a miscarriage or early baby loss. As a friend you may be closer than a family member. As a colleague you may be closer than a friend or neighbour. It is not the label that determines your place in the radius but your relationship with the people at the centre.

However close you are to someone who has had a miscarriage or early baby loss, be guided by the bereaved parents in how you respond. One of the real difficulties for the person you love who is going through miscarriage is that no one else knows what they have lost. Miscarriage is a very private affair but it is also a very real bereavement. Very few people will have any understanding of the extent of the "emotional investment" they have made in the new life, the baby, who was growing inside them.

Be reassured, most people find it difficult to know how to react or what to say. It is enough, if you are struggling, to say, "I am sorry for your loss" or, "That must have been awful for you..." and let them respond.

Be guided by their words. Only they know what that pregnancy and child meant to them, their hopes and dreams. Only they know how much they have lost. As one specialist on bereavement said,
"When you lose a parent you lose your past.
When you lose a child you lose your future."

Pastoral guidance for everyone who cares

Whatever your relationship to the family of the baby who has been lost, you will have your own feelings, about them and about what has happened. The most important thing to know is that they are feeling hurt. They may be feeling bewildered, because what, after all, has been lost? They may just have discovered the pregnancy, only to have it snatched away. Their feelings may be confused. They will almost certainly be reeling from the shock.

You may feel that you do not want to hurt them any more by mentioning it. But, believe me, there is nothing more you can do to increase the pain they are already feeling than to ignore what has happened to them.

> You're rarely going to be wrong if you offer some acknowledgment... It doesn't need to be long or complex, but it needs to be said. It can be as short as "I'm sorry you are going through this." It will make a difference.
>
> Once you acknowledge it, move from talking to listening. Take your cue from the grieving person about what they're willing to talk about. If they want to open up, ask them about the person or pet they lost. Ask them what they miss most. But don't push. The goal is to be half a step behind and not to lead them anywhere.[5]

It will not be easy. But it you care you cannot *not* mention it. If you can "be present" to them in their pain that will be a real gift.

The importance of listening

Being really "present" includes really listening. This is not the usual daily listening where we hear and respond with our own thoughts and ideas.

When we are with someone who needs to grieve, we need to listen deeply or "actively".[6] This means listening to understand rather than to fix; listening to enter their world rather than to respond with our own experience and our own solutions; and listening out for the feelings behind the words. It is a particular skill and some people find it easier than others. It is a surprising paradox that really caring people often find this the hardest listening to do because they so want to fix everyone's problems.

If the bereaved parents do not want to talk they will let you know. If they do, then, hard as it may be, listen. I mean listen without speaking, without interruptions. This is not about you or about making sure you get the story straight in your head. This is about them. They have suffered a major loss. They may still be working out the story in their own minds – try not to interfere with questions. Give them time to think, to speak, to cry and to be silent.

This pain they are in will not go away quickly. They may need time off; they may need expert help with grief counselling. But you, as one of their circle of family and friends, can do a great deal to help by simply listening, as hard as that may be.

What NOT to say

"It happens all the time."

"One in four pregnancies ends in miscarriage."

"You're young – you'll get over it."

"My mum/sister/girlfriend/flatmate had a miscarriage and she was fine."

"It was very early, so can't have been fully formed."
(They will hear this as "not a real baby".)

"There must have been something wrong with it."

"It was just a bundle of cells at that stage."

"At least you know you can get pregnant!"

"You can always have another."

"Time will heal."

"Let me know when you feel better and we'll get together."
(They will hear this as "I do not want to be with you in your pain, only in good times.")

"Have a drink/cake/some chocolate and cheer up!"

"It could be worse."

"It was a blessing in disguise."

These words and phrases are experienced as avoidant or dismissive and will not help those who need to grieve.

DO say:

"How are you?" And then listen...

"That must have been so difficult."
And then listen...

"Would you like to say what happened?"
And then listen...

These are responses that allow grace
into the pain. They actualise God's love
in a real way in real time for that
grieving person.

I remember being visited by someone from a local baby loss charity who first told me how important it is to allow our feelings. She had once been chided by nurses because a woman she visited cried for the first time after her baby loss. The hospital thought that the volunteer had "made her cry". In fact she had allowed the woman to feel what she was feeling so that healing could happen. Hard as it might be to bear, their tears are a good sign.

Your supportive, kind, listening and attentive presence now can be a very powerful service to the bereaved parents and their family. When we help people to bear their burdens, to feel what they feel, to tell the story and to remember we are really acting as God's agents on earth. It is that important.

You may want to encourage them to cry if they want to. Not everyone feels comfortable crying and this will depend on you and them and your feelings and experience.

Help them to remember

If the bereaved parents trust you and are talking to you, you might feel there comes a time when it is okay to ask further questions to help them to get the story straight in their minds:

- Do you have a name for your baby?

- How would you like to remember her/him? (Avoid referring to the baby as "it" – say instead, "Did you feel your baby was a girl or a boy?")

- Would it help you to write a letter to your baby?

- Would you like to write down the story of what happened?

- Would you like to make a book or a memory box of any mementos you may have? (They may have scan pictures, bootees, a hospital wrist band, ante-natal appointment cards, greetings cards, sympathy cards...)

- Would you like to have a prayer service or a Mass for your baby?

- Would you like to make your own certificate to recognise your baby's existence?

- Would you like to draw, paint or compose something (or is there any other activity that might create a memory of the child)?

Your gentle presence may also be very helpful when the time comes for them to start to face the world again. This cannot be rushed. Ask them if they would like to go somewhere, for instance, to buy a lovely book where they can begin to write down all their thoughts and feelings and the story of the pregnancy.

In a nutshell, the role of anyone who wants to help support a woman or a couple who have experienced any early baby loss is to help them to facilitate their own processing of what happened.

They, the bereaved parents, are the ones who have to do the hard "feeling" work. It is understandable if they want to bypass their feelings. You may also need to make sure that they are not using their time to drink or eat their way out of this dreadful moment.

I too wish I could "make it better" for them, and for you. I know what a hard place you are all in in your different ways. I pray as I write that you find exactly what you need.

I pray that if you do not find what you need, if things seem to go awry in your relationships as you all struggle with this devastating event in your lives, that you can turn to God and the consolations of the Church.

Endnotes

1   http://jumelle.ca/2012/11/10/grieving-grandparents/

2   www.catholicgrandparentsassociation.com

3   https://www.miscarriageassociation.org.uk/

4   Stephen McGann's mother found her babies' unmarked grave much later in her own life: https://www.itv.com/loosewomen/call-the-midwife-actor-stephen-mcgann-my-twin-brothers-tragically-died-at-birth

5   Dr Patrick O'Malley, "Getting Grief Right": http://drpatrickomalley.com/blog/

6   https://www.psychologytoday.com/blog/the-empowerment-diary/201708/deep-listening-in-personal-relationships?destination=node/1105349

4

The paradox of grief

The paradox of grief is that in the midst of love and beauty we find loss and grief and in the midst of loss and grief we also have love and beauty. I hesitate to include this in a book on baby loss but your child is and always has been a blessing to you and to your whole family, even if it feels too raw right now. It is okay not to feel okay with this – I include these words for the future if and when you are ready for them.

There was beauty there, there was a precious life there, and one day you may feel able to thank God for the gift of the life given to you even for such a short period of time. You will be glad for the love that created her/him and for the time that you carried him/her deep inside you. If you never feel that, that is okay too. You are what you are and that is beautiful in the sight of God. You are loved by God as you are, not as you would like to be.

These are only my words, a very long time after my own baby losses. It will not feel like that to the bereaved parent at this time. It may never feel like that for them. It is not yours to say or to know, it is theirs. Remember, "tread softly", for you tread on their dreams.

Everyone will have their own thoughts and beliefs about what their loss means. So, if you are a friend or family member, think before you speak. Your words may help, but they may not and the possibility of doing damage to the bereaved parents by interfering with their ability to feel the pain of grief is great. Tread carefully and be guided in your response by the bereaved parents themselves.

I believe that God is compassion and love. I believe that God feels our pain and knows all our needs; that God has loved you and your child from before he made you. In Psalm 139 the psalmist says to God: "It was you who formed my inward parts; you knit me together in my mother's womb." God has held, and still holds, you and your child in his strong and gentle hands. As you love and miss your child, so God loves you. God's arms are big enough and God loves you with a mother's and a father's love.

Can we make sense of our suffering? I don't think we can, for anyone else. It is a road we each have to travel. I now think that there is something powerful in the Incarnation that can speak to us. "Incarnation" literally means "enflesh", to "become flesh": Jesus, made man, God "in skin", is one like us, in our pain. Yet it was Mary, at the foot of the cross, who was with me as I sat with our daughter in her cot in the special care unit.

If someone had tried to talk to me about God at the time of my losses it would not have helped. I believe and believing helps me. But however much we believe we know what someone needs, no one who is grieving wants to be preached at. If you care, do the hard work of being a compassionate listener rather than a "Job's comforter".[1]

What we say may or may not be true but as, poet and Trappist monk Thomas Merton warned, the "sword of truth" is sharp.
It needs to be very, very carefully wielded. Is it better to be right or to love? To me, I will probably always say "to love", because love is the ultimate truth.

So if someone comes to you after losing a baby, perhaps sobbing in grief, do not tell them immediately about God's love and that their baby is in heaven. Instead, if you can, hold them and let them cry. Let them know that they are loved as they are in all their distress. That sharp distress will go away but it will take time: God's time, not your time. God's love is not an abstract notion: it needs to be made real by our living, loving, everyday actions. If God loves them, it is not for us to shut them up, but to allow them to feel the pain they are feeling. So hold them, on God's behalf, in love as they grieve.

Remembering

"Can a woman forget... the child of her womb?
Even these may forget, yet I will not forget you."

Isaiah 49:15

Every year for the rest of your life the day you lost your baby will come around again. Mother's Day, Father's Day, due dates, Christmas... seasons of joy are also seasons of loss for anyone who has suffered a baby loss. It will help to have done the hard "feeling" work of grieving in the early days and of telling the story and making sense of what happened and what your loss means to you.

It helped me enormously when, years later, I was able to pray about and name each of the babies lost in miscarriage, a form of spiritual baptism. If you want to write a card or create a "birth certificate" you can do so. Keep all these treasures in a beautiful memory box. It can be as large or as small as you like. Use an old cardboard box and make it a couple or a family activity to decorate it.

Mark the date on the calendar and have it repeat yearly, with reminders on your phone. Remember your baby at special family times. Light a candle and say a prayer, take part in a specially dedicated church service, bake a cake, or whatever you wish. How you do this will also help your other children, family and friends to keep your baby in their mind and in their prayers. And if you cannot do this, that is okay too. Your baby does not need you to do anything.
The remembering is to help you, not them.

"Your Father knows what you need before you ask him."

Matthew 6:8

There are as many ways of remembering the babies we have lost as there are babies. You will feel your own way forward with this, or ask for help from a kind or creative person. These are just a few basic ideas to get you started:

- Light a candle: While I was struggling to come to terms with our losses I was helped most by a woman I met just once in a social work or an NHS role (it was a long time ago: I cannot remember all the details). The funeral was over and no one wanted to know any more. I had gone to a clinic and she surprised me by being deeply understanding of our difficulty. She said something so simple, that I had not even thought of but that helped me enormously. She said that her sister had died and when she wanted to remember her she lit a candle.

- Have a memorial service: Ben Fogle and his wife Marina had a memorial service on the anniversary of their baby's death. "We lost him at eight months or so. It's someone you nearly met, you dreamed of meeting, you projected what your family would be like, you projected the three children together, you did the nursery, you'd told the children... To have that stolen from you is painful in a way that, unless you've been through it yourself, you can't understand and that's why we've spoken about it."[2]

- Have a Mass or special service said on the anniversary of the baby's due date or the date of the loss or the date you found out you were pregnant. Or any time that feels right for you. It can be as private as you wish. It may be helpful for family and friends to remember and to be reminded that your family is greater than its visible parts.

40

- Mother's and Father's days can be particularly difficult, so this is a good time to plan something small, like lighting a candle, to remember your baby.

- Make a Christmas tree ornament: that way every year your baby is remembered with love in the midst of the family celebrations for the birth of our Saviour.

- Put your story into words or pictures, or any creative format you prefer, and look at that when you feel the need to reconnect.

- If you want to share your story more widely, Tommy's is an organisation which is challenging the stigma around speaking about baby loss. On its website there is a section where you can share your story.[3]

Moving on

You want the baby you lost; you want a baby; a family; you want to complete your family. You may be in a hurry and feel that time is running out for you. Whatever your situation, your age and your desires, if you want to have more children do try to prepare yourself as well as you can. Time is a real issue for women and fertility and I know what it feels like to have loss after loss and years going by.

The truth is that if we try to curtail our grief, or to move on too quickly, it can have a big impact on the children we have after such a profound loss. Sheila, Dennis and Matthew Linn address this problem directly where they acknowledge that "if parents have not grieved for a lost baby, they are less likely to be emotionally available to fully bond with subsequent children". As if to confirm the twin loss story (see Life Stories, page 47), the Linns say that "children are very sensitive to the loss of siblings, even when they have not been told about such losses."[4]

There is no easy answer to this and no child is born into a trouble-free world. So do not beat yourself up over this. It is enough for you to allow yourself to grieve and not to worry about the future. In fact, allowing yourself to grieve is the best way to prepare for the future.

When you have a new baby you will want to love that child fully for themselves. When you have small children you may want to tell them about their brother or sister in heaven. When and how you do this will be managed best by having grieved properly (as in having allowed the feelings of grief and told the story as much as you need to) before they are born. Trust yourself and your own feelings. Get help if you want it. Many people carry burdens they may feel inadequate for. Your new children are a sign of hope and every new person comes with their own inbuilt strengths and resiliences.

After Bowlby, who identified the damage done to children separated from their parents at certain formative stages of their lives,[5] came Winnicott. Winnicott, without denying the attachment impact of early childhood loss and separation, pointed out that it is also true that children are naturally resilient and are usually fine as long as they get "good enough" parenting.[6]

In this, as in so many other areas, this quote from Teddy Roosevelt speaks to us: "Do the best you can, with what you have, where you are."

There are healing actions you may want to do with your little children if it feels right for you. This is taken from Sheila, Dennis and Matthew Linn:[7]

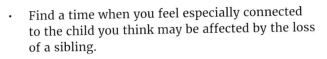

- Find a time when you feel especially connected to the child you think may be affected by the loss of a sibling.

- Create a safe and warm environment, in which your child's favourite dolls or stuffed animals are nearby.

- Tell your child as much as you know about the loss.

- Ask your child if any of the dolls or stuffed animals want to say anything, or if he or she wants to say anything to, or do anything with, the dolls or stuffed animals. Follow the child's lead, and mirror back to the child any feelings he or she expresses.

- Talk over with the child what name to give the lost sibling.

- During the next days and weeks, offer the child additional opportunities to express any feelings about the loss with the help of the dolls or stuffed animals.

Endnotes

1. Job 16:2

2. http://www.huffingtonpost.co.uk/2015/07/27/ben-fogle-this-morning-interview-death-unborn-son_n_7877972.html?ir=UK+Lifestyle&

3. https://www.tommys.org/our-organisation/about-us/campaigns/miscourage-campaign/share-miscourage-story

4. Sheila, Dennis and Matthew Linn, *Already Home: Receiving Healing from the Near-Death Experience Without Having to Die*, chapter 15.

5. For a description of Bowlby's Attachment Theory, see: https://www.simplypsychology.org/bowlby.html

6. D.W. Winnicott, *The Child, the Family and the Outside World* (London: Penguin, 1973); see also Bruno Bethelheim, *A Good Parent* (London: Thames & Hudson, 1987).

7. Sheila, Dennis and Matthew Linn (*Already Home.*)

5

Life stories

When I read leaflets on grief they sometimes seem to speak of it in ways that can make it seem a little antiseptic, or anodyne, or even noble and beautiful. My experience of grief was none of those things. Your reality now is that your arms may ache for the baby you cannot hold. There may not even be a funeral. The loss is, in every way, internal to you and to your spouse or partner. It can feel as if you have been scooped into an alternative universe of just you two and your pain, a hell on earth. You can look out and see people and they can see you but they cannot see the hell around you. Your story, like everyone else's, is unique.

Memories

A long time ago, over a period of about three or four years and very early on in our marriage, I had four miscarriages. Some happened alone at home and I remember the difficulty of telling my husband. At least one required hospitalisation and a D&C (dilation and curettage). I no longer have a clear memory of each separate miscarriage but some moments stand out in my memory: the shock of going to the toilet one day and just painlessly losing the pregnancy in a rush of blood; the shame of being summoned, wearing just a scanty hospital gown, from my hospital bed following a D&C to a dingy side room by a well-spoken, well-dressed woman in pearls who told me briskly that it was time to stop trying to have my own babies and to plan for adoption instead. "It is not going to happen, is it?" she said. I did not object to adoption, but I bristled at the lack of care she had shown for my condition or my feelings. I was heartbroken but I found it difficult to share my feelings, or, even then, to recognise that these miscarriages were significant life events.

It was not until our healthy full-term daughter died, eight days after her birth, that I was overwhelmed by the sense of her loss and of all the losses I had ever suffered but never really acknowledged at the time because I did not know how to grieve. In those days feelings were not accepted in the wider culture as they are now. My family of origin were stressed and poor and had no time to "indulge" feelings.

Our daughter's natural birth was a car crash and she and I were both in need of immediate and urgent medical interventions. Thankfully we were kept in the same hospital. I was awoken in the middle of the night a few days after she was born and taken down to her cot in the special care unit where the "on call" priest quickly baptised her. We went through the motions but no one really knew how to help us to process what was happening. In the middle of the night she died I was hurriedly discharged from the hospital. It was Christmas and it seemed that all the world was laughing and having a good time while we looked on from our devastation.

People tried to help. One person told me how she had had a miscarriage once and it had not bothered her at all. I heard about King David who got up and got on with his life after his son's death as it was now too late to change the facts. One or two dared to be with us as we wept and tried to come to terms with what had happened to us. For those kind and brave people I was, and am, very grateful indeed.

My story, much longer than I can say here, still lives in me, carried in my heart. I have learned to live and to laugh with everyone else but I know now that none of us is very far from tragedy.

"People change, and smile: but the agony abides."

T.S. Eliot, "The Dry Salvages",
Four Quartets

I believe that all our babies in heaven are also always with me, yet most people will never know that. Sometimes this upsets me, but I also believe that there is a much bigger story here than any one of us can see. As St Paul said, we see dimly through a glass. I believe that no tiny life, anywhere on earth or in the heavens, exists without God's love. Nothing is wasted in God's economy. Everything is drawn back to our loving creator God. And we too will, I hope and I trust, be drawn back to our loving creator God when our time on earth is up. Can anyone prove me wrong? Not yet. So I continue to believe and to pray and to look forward to the moment when I too am pulled into God's loving embrace with my babies who are already there.

Life story: "I named her Rosie"

The very first person I told about this book on miscarriage told me that her first pregnancy had ended in miscarriage. Like mine, it happened when she went to the toilet. Unlike mine, she experienced some pains, which she said were probably mini-contractions. She subsequently made a little angel tree decoration and wrote her daughter's name on it. "I did not know my baby was a girl", she told me. "I just felt it, so I named her Rosie and made the decoration. We hang it on the Christmas tree every year and the children know who it is for and what it means to me."

Life story: the missing twin

My second child was thought to have been a twin early in the pregnancy. I never told him as a child but somehow my son has always believed that he had a twin who died before birth. Even now I worry when he rings because I feel he has a very fragile hold on life. It is difficult to explain but I worry more about him – when he rings I always think there is something wrong and I put this down to losing his twin even though it was very early in the pregnancy. This is something I have never spoken about even to my husband.

Life story: "I blamed myself"

"I had several miscarriages but the last was in the late 1970s. All were early, around eight weeks of pregnancy, but in each case I knew that I was pregnant, although I was told on occasion that perhaps I hadn't been. There was no support that I remember, in fact very little even when I had a baby who survived for only three days in intensive care in 1978.

"The effect on me was that of fear whenever I went to the toilet in early pregnancy lest I see the first signs of miscarriage. I blamed myself and wondered what I had done or not done to cause it. I was reluctant to let anyone know I was pregnant until any pregnancy was over twelve weeks. (I remember that Princess Diana announced her pregnancy with William at a much earlier date than I did, although William is six weeks younger than my middle daughter.) I was lucky to have a very supportive husband, but knowing how much he cared I did not like to grieve too openly and upset him.

"Professionally I have also worked with those who have gone through a miscarriage. Perhaps one very important thing is to give permission to talk, discuss and cry if needed. So often, people try to either pretend it didn't really matter because 'it wasn't really a baby yet', or try to cheer you up, tell you to concentrate on the good things you have and forget the bad. There is a point, of course, when some need professional help to move on with life, but grieving isn't an optional extra.

"I also remember one girl whom I saw because she was pregnant and unsure about keeping the baby. When she had a miscarriage later, she felt guilty because she had not wanted the baby. (She later went on to have other children.) Some miscarriages happen at a later stage in the pregnancy: this has its own medical and emotional effects.

"I have to say that after the birth and death of my first child, I felt the miscarriages were – how can I put it – less important in comparison: after all, I had carried her for nine months and there seemed no reason why anything should go wrong.

"For anyone seeking to support someone who has had a miscarriage, I would say, 'Listen. Don't try to reassure or comfort, but be there for her, know who to refer to (voluntary agencies, and NHS) and don't forget that partners, other children perhaps, grandparents, all may also need support. Oh, yes, and remember that miscarriage is actually quite common. Having had one miscarriage does not mean a mum won't have another, although I think these days there is much more investigation into possible reasons, and helpful treatment, to prevent future miscarriages.'"

Life story: a bereavement, not a disappointment

"I miscarried my first child. I found it was a very traumatic experience. I had been bleeding for two weeks and then was taken into hospital. When it was finally confirmed that I had miscarried, I was distraught and sobbing. But then I was surprised to find that I had periods of calm but, without warning, I would be beside myself with grief. I remember a nursing assistant explaining to me that grief came in waves and that the breaks in the distress were very normal. I found it so reassuring to understand what was happening.

"Many people said the usual inappropriate things about being able to have another or it's nature's way of getting rid of a child with disabilities. I think it is very hard for people, myself included, to understand that I was grieving for that particular child and that even at that early stage I felt such powerful feelings for a child I had not yet seen or held.

"It sometimes felt as though people regarded the pregnancy as something not quite real. It was as if it was a plan that hadn't worked out rather than a bereavement. So in responding to miscarriage, I think it is important to treat it as a bereavement rather than some kind of disappointment.

"One thing I did appreciate was people who asked how I was or how I was feeling but in a normal conversational way which gave me scope to talk about it or not depending on how I felt.

"I think it is helpful to give someone the option of visits or company rather than assume it's better to call in. I had people visit who did want to acknowledge what had happened, but I was very weepy and distraught and just felt I needed time to cry on my own. This was difficult with people with whom I didn't feel comfortable enough to be expressing so much emotion. I didn't have control of it and also didn't want to cause them distress."

Life story: "I should have understood"

"I have a daughter who lost a baby early in the pregnancy and I don't think I supported her properly. Because it was fairly early I don't think I really understood her pain or I didn't feel I could say or do anything. It was only when she put on Facebook later that it would have been her due date that I realised the depth of her pain and by then it was too late to help. I should have understood and talked to her but I didn't. Perhaps it was easier for us both not to talk about it, but had we talked what could have been said? She knew after the loss that I was sad and that I was there for her but what was to be said? Even now we don't talk about it."

Life story: "my body remembers"

"My story goes back a very long way. We were very young and so keen to have a baby. My first two pregnancies ended in miscarriage and to this day I can remember the feelings of desolation. More than forty years on it is as if my body remembers as I find myself thinking of those lost babies at the times of the miscarriages without having made any conscious effort to do so.

"Those around me offered the usual platitudes about it being nature's way and I found no compassionate listener. In fact a close friend was exasperated at my grief and told me in no uncertain terms to pull myself together. Only recently, when her young daughter-in-law had a miscarriage, did she say to me how sorry she was at her impatience as she had no idea how much the loss could hurt.

"Subsequently we went on to have five lovely children and have been so blessed. I hope and think maybe there is nowadays more understanding and compassion about miscarriages."

"So often, people try to either pretend it didn't really matter because 'it wasn't really a baby yet', or try to cheer you up; tell you to concentrate on the good things you have and forget the bad. There is a point, of course, when some need professional help to move on with life, but grieving isn't an optional extra."

A grieving mother

6

Prayers and blessings

Ideally all loss will be adequately mourned. I have detailed the importance of this and outlined some characteristics of what it means to grieve, or to mourn our lost children. We can also pray for healing of unresolved grief in ourselves as well as any residual and unresolved grief our parents may have experienced that also affects us.

The best book I have found on this is the Linns' paperback *Healing Our Beginning*.[1] This short book contains some simple prayers to be said alone or with a trusted friend to heal us from past trauma surrounding birth and loss. One aspect it deals with that most books seem to ignore is the impact of the loss of one twin, both on the parents and subsequent children, but also, very importantly, on the surviving twin. "Children", they write, "are very sensitive to the loss of siblings, even when they have not been told about such losses."

They outline short healing processes, in the Ignatian style, for the loss of one's own baby, or for a lost sibling, and which follow simple patterns of visualisation.[2]

Another useful source is the website for the United States Conference of Catholic Bishops, which has a simple ritual for the blessing of parents after a miscarriage or stillbirth.

Healing Process [3]

1. Light a candle. Close your eyes and breathe deeply. Recall a moment in your life when you experienced love. Breathe this love into yourself once again.

2. Get in touch with your feelings regarding the baby that you lost (love, sadness, longing, grief, guilt, anger, curiosity, etc.).

3. See someone you love standing before you, holding your child and offering him or her to you. This could be a deceased relative or beloved friend, a trusted religious figure, etc. Open your arms and receive the child. Or perhaps your child is older now and walks towards you.

4. Ask what name he or she wishes to be called. You may want to use some ritual that is meaningful to you and consistent with your beliefs to welcome and bless the child.

5. Say and do with the child all that your heart longs for, and let the child do the same for you.

6. Talk over with the child how you can continue to be together. How do you want the child to love and be present to you and your family? How does the child want you to love and be present to him or her?

7. When you are ready, place the child back in the care of whoever offered the child to you. See that, instead of walking away from you, they walk *towards* you right into your heart. Feel their warm presence as they make their home in your heart. Breathe deeply, allowing that warmth to fill your whole body.

Other Healing Actions

You may wish to go to one of your favourite places, where you feel most able to give and receive love. In your spirit invite your child to accompany you. Share with the child why this place means so much to you.

Endnotes

1   Sheila Fabricant Linn, Dennis Linn and Matthew Linn, *Healing Our Beginning* (New Jersey: Paulist Press, 2005).

2   For the full meditation see *Healing Our Beginning*, 40.

3   Sheila, Dennis and Matthew Linn, from *Healing Our Beginning*.

Resources and references

Books

- **Diana Crossley and Kate Sheppard**, *Muddles, Puddles and Sunshine* (Stroud: Hawthorn Press, 2000). For adults to use with children. Not specifically on early baby loss but contains ideas and exercises to help children think, talk about and remember someone who has died.

- **Alix Henley and Nancy Kohner,** *When a Baby Dies: the experience of late miscarriage, stillbirth and neonatal death* (London: Routledge, 2001). This has more real-life stories and more on understanding the medical terminology and practicalities such as considering the future.

- **Clara Hinton,** *Silent Grief: Miscarriage – Child Loss: finding your way through the darkness* (Green Forest: New Leaf Press, 1998). This has a more conversational approach with lots of biblical quotes and real-life stories.

- **Tim Nelson,** *A Guide for Fathers: when a baby dies* (St Paul: Tim Nelson, 2004).

- **Joey O'Connor,** *Children and Grief: helping your child understand death* (Grand Rapids: Fleming H. Revell, 2004). A father and pastor writes to help parents to help their children understand and face loss.

Websites

- **Apostolate of Hannah's Tears:** http://hannahstears.net/
  Offers prayer support and comfort to the broken-hearted who
  suffer the pains of infertility at any stage of life, difficult pregnancy,
  miscarriage, stillbirth, the loss of a child and the adoption process.

- **A Blog for Fathers When a Baby Dies:**
  fathersgrievinginfantloss.blogspot.co.uk

- **Catholic Miscarriage Support:**
  http://www.catholicmiscarriagesupport.com/
  Practical and spiritual support for Catholics who have
  lost a child to miscarriage.

- **Child Bereavement:** www.childbereavementuk.org
  Supports families and educates professionals when a baby
  or child of any age dies or is dying, or when a child is
  facing bereavement.

- **Compassionate Friends:** www.tcf.org.uk
  Offers support after the death of a child at any age.

- **Gingerbread:** www.gingerbread.org.uk/information/bereavement/
  Offers practical advice and factsheets for families
  facing bereavement.

- **Tommy's:** www.tommys.org
  Funds research into miscarriage, stillbirth and premature
  birth, and provides pregnancy health information to parents.
  Tommy's also has a remembrance page to which you can
  add your own story.

- **The Remembrance Book at 'A place to remember':**
  http://www.aplacetoremember.com/remembrance.html
  This site sells mementos but is also another place where
  you can share your baby loss story.

- **Winston's Wish:** www.winstonswish.org
  Offers help for anyone supporting bereaved children
  and young people.